Creating America

A History of the United States

McDougal Littell

Evanston, Illinois • Boston • Dallas

Printed in the United States of America

ISBN 0-618-19402-9

5 6 7 8 9 - DWI - 04 03

Contents

To the Teacher

In this booklet, you will find instructions, forms, and scoring suggestions for use in setting up and evaluating alternative assessments for *Creating America: A History of the United States*. After an introduction to formal and alternative assessment types, alternative assessment is discussed and implemented under three main headings.

Process Assessment

Process assessment refers to observing students as they work. Your aim is to see how well they think through the assignment, carry it out, work together, and solve problems that arise. This booklet has forms to help you observe and evaluate students' participation in group discussions and in cooperative activities.

Product and Performance Assessment

Product and performance assessment focuses on the end results of students' work. Beginning with forms for students to use in planning group projects, this section contains guidance in assessing individual and group projects as well as oral presentations. It also includes forms for students to use in evaluating their own performances and those of their peers.

Portfolio Assessment

In portfolio assessment, you and your students review and evaluate the students' work together. Forms in this section help students select and evaluate the portfolios, provide you and your students with standards for evaluating portfolios, and give students an opportunity to review with their families what they have accomplished.

Activity Options Assessment

The Activity Options at the end of each section of *Creating America* offers opportunities for students to demonstrate learning through interdisciplinary activities. Each activity has a rubric assigned to it to aid you in evaluating the student's product or performance. The activities fall into five main categories: Art Type activities, Information Assessing, Oral Presentations, Writing Activities, and Technology Activities.

Assessment of student learning may take place in a variety of ways. The chart on the following page will show you the assessment options in *Creating America*. Notice that the assessment can take place in many ways, from informal checks to formal quizzes and tests. The forms and instructions in this book will help you to implement many of them.

Assessment Options for *Creating America*

Assessment Type	Student Edition	Teacher's Edition	Ancillaries
Ongoing, Informal	• Reading History • Skillbuilder questions • Geography Skillbuilder • History Through Art • *America's History Makers* • Interactive Primary Sources • Section Assessment • Chapter Assessment	• Time Line discussion • Assess and Reteach in each section	• *In-Depth* Resources Guided Reading, Skillbuilder practice, Geography Application, Reteaching Activity, Vocabulary Builder • *America's History Makers* • *Outline Map Activities*
Alternative	• Interact with History • Skillbuilder Handbook exercises • History Workshop • Interdisciplinary Challenge • Activity Options in Section Assessment • Alternative Assessment Activities in the Chapter Assessment	• Interdisciplinary Challenge Standards for Evaluation • Activity Options Rubrics • Skillbuilder Mini-Lesson	• *In-Depth Resources* Primary Sources, Literature selections, Enrichment Activity • *Economics in History* • *Interdisciplinary Projects* • *Why It Matters Now* • *Integrated Assessment*
Formal			• *Formal Assessment* Section quizzes Chapter tests (Forms A and B) • *Test Maker* (software) • *Preparing for Standardized Tests*

Introduction to Integrated Assessment

What is happening in the world of assessment? Until recently, formal assessments, primarily paper-and-pencil tests, have been the most popular way to measure a student's progress in school. Their popularity stems from their ease of use and their application as an objective measuring instrument. They are based on the belief that the knowledge a student has acquired is the most accurate indication of his or her success in school.

Over time, educators have begun to want more information about their students than could be gleaned from formal assessment and, as a result, have sought ways to get a broader view of their students' skills and abilities. They want assessment to mirror what they see from their students every day in the classroom. Many teachers have turned to alternative assessments that involve students in complex, multimodal activities. These assessments help teachers see their students holistically as critical thinkers, problem solvers, and acquirers of knowledge. Alternative assessment is sometimes called *authentic* or *performance-based assessment*.

Formal and Alternative Assessments

Although they may be seen as opposing methods, formal and alternative assessments are not necessarily in conflict. They are different ways of measuring student performance, with different goals and outcomes. A complete assessment program includes both formal and alternative assessments; a complete student profile includes results from both kinds of instruments.

Throughout *Creating America*, you will find opportunities for both formal and alternative assessments. By using a mixture of assessment types, you and your students, together, can develop a comprehensive account of the students' progress in learning history.

The diagrams on the next two pages offer a more complete description of these two major assessment types.

Formal Assessment

Four types of formal assessment instruments are commonly used.

Standardized Tests
- measure a student's performance in various knowledge and skill areas against students in other districts or across the country
- compare results with national norms
- example: nationally published standardized tests given once a year

Criterion-Referenced Tests
- measure whether a student has attained mastery of instructional objectives
- compare results with a set percentage score
- examples: classroom, school, or district tests that measure specified instructional objectives

FORMAL ASSESSMENT

Program Tests, Teacher-Made Tests
- measure a student's retention and comprehension of specific content
- examples: Section Quizzes and Chapter Tests for *Creating America*

Essay Tests
- measure a student's ability to express himself or herself in writing, given a specific assignment
- measure some content knowledge
- example: placement exams

Characteristics of Formal Assessment

1. Formal assessment asks the student: What do you know? Its primary purpose is to measure how much knowledge a student has retained from what has been taught.

2. The emphasis is on recall, generally demonstrated in paper-and-pencil tests. The tests often include matching, true-false, and multiple-choice items.

3. The tests are usually timed, giving students a limited amount of time in which to show what they know.

4. Formal assessment allows for comparisons. In standardized tests, a student's results are compared with national norms; in criterion-referenced tests, the results are compared with a percentage score that is said to indicate mastery. When these tests are used, it is possible to compare a student's performance with that of other students in the classroom, the district, or the country.

Alternative Assessment

The techniques and instruments associated with alternative assessment fall into three main categories.

Process Assessment

- requires students to demonstrate or share their processes, behaviors, strategies, and critical thinking abilities as they work to understand skills and concepts
- focuses the teacher's attention on student processes, behaviors, and strategies rather than on the final results
  - is based on judgment guided by criteria
    - examples: group discussion, cooperative activity

Product and Performance Assessment

- requires students to produce a tangible product or to create a performance that demonstrates their understanding of skills and concepts
- focuses the teacher's attention on the final results rather than on the processes students used to create them
  - is based on judgment guided by criteria
    - examples: essay, speech, model

ALTERNATIVE ASSESSMENT

Portfolio Assessment

- a purposeful collection of student work that exhibits the student's overall efforts, progress, and achievements over time in one or more areas of the curriculum
  - examples: reports, maps, time lines, essays, models, videos, journals, poems, reviews

Characteristics of Alternative Assessment

1. Alternative assessment asks students: What can you do? and How do you do it? Its primary purpose is to give a broad picture of the student as a critical thinker, problem solver, and learner.

2. The tasks and experiences used for alternative assessment are already familiar to students. They include the variety of activities found in most classrooms, such as projects, models, simulations, role-plays, discussions, and other forms of expression.

3. Alternative assessment is ongoing. Students have the opportunity to show what they can do in a variety of tasks over time.

4. Both teachers and students are actively involved in alternative assessment. Reflection, self-assessment, observation, and participation are at the heart of the process.

5. Alternative assessment is holistic. Teachers use many different methods to get a full picture of a student's performance.

Process Assessment: Observing Students in Progress

This chapter focuses attention on observing students in the process of understanding and communicating rather than on assessing the final results. You might call this "watching minds at work" or "observing work in progress." The emphasis is on understanding the behaviors, strategies, and critical thinking skills your students use as they read, write, communicate, and participate in class activities.

The key to process assessment lies in your own observational and conferencing skills. In regular classroom situations, you will have many opportunities to learn more about your students. You can begin process assessment by asking questions like the following about a student's processes, strategies, and behaviors.

- What reading strategies does the student use to develop interpretations of a text?
- Does the student invest himself or herself in a task?
- Does the student demonstrate effective problem-solving strategies?
- Does the student have good collaborative work habits?
- What processes does the student use to write an essay?

The key to process assessment lies in your own observational and conferencing skills.

- Does the student participate well in class discussions?
- How does the student respond and react during conferences?
- Is the student developing his or her own criteria and standards for evaluation?
- How does the student respond to peer reviews?

Characteristics of Process Assessment

1. In process assessment, there are no test items. The assessment requires either observation of students in action or review of work in progress, such as drafts created in the process of writing an essay or outlines and note cards written for a research report.

2. Assessment formats include scales, checklists, and anecdotal records.

3. The evaluation focuses on a student's ability to apply higher-level thinking skills to a task rather than on his or her ability to recall information or to perform specific skills.

4. The evaluation focuses on a student's processes, behavior, and strategies rather than on the final results of the process. This is not to suggest that final results are not important; they simply aren't the focus of this kind of assessment.

Assessing Reading and Writing Processes

Because reading and writing occupy much of your students' time in history, it is worthwhile to observe their behaviors and strategies in these activities.

1. Observe your students while they are reading. Discover as much as you can about whether your students enjoy the process, approach it with purpose, apply prior knowledge, make connections to personal experiences, make and test predictions while they read, revise interpretations as they learn new information, review facts, form opinions, and stay on task.

2. To help students focus their attention while they read, have them use the Guided Reading sheets in the *In-Depth Resources*. Go over these sheets with the students in conferences periodically.

3. Observe your students while they are writing. Notice whether your students are actively involved, think and plan effectively, experiment, ask for teacher and peer feedback, revise drafts, proofread carefully, and share their finished work with others.

4. Review note cards, outlines, and drafts your students create during the writing process.

Assessing Planning and Organizational Skills

Understanding how students plan and organize work will tell you a great deal about their approach to new tasks. When you meet with them for progress reports, go over their action plans and task sheets. Help them evaluate the effectiveness of their strategies and processes. You can have students complete and share with you the Project Proposal and Action Plan on page 11 and the Task Sheet for a Group Project on page 12 in the next section of this book.

Assessing Cooperative Learning and Group Discussions

Pay close attention to how your students interact with each other and what they learn from one another in collaborative projects, small groups, class discussions, and peer reviews. For checklists, use Standards for Evaluating a Cooperative Activity and Standards for Evaluating a Group Discussion, which follow.

Support for Process Assessment in *Creating America*

Creating America provides opportunities for process assessment throughout the program.

- "Key Questions" identified in the Teacher's Edition for every section are suggestions for class discussions.
- *Activity Options* ideas appear in every section of the Student Edition.
- *In-Depth Resources* for each unit provide Guided Reading sheets for every section.
- Chapter Activities on every chapter assessment in the student edition provide many opportunities to observe students in action.

Using the Forms to Assess Processes

- Work with students to create the rubric you will use to evaluate behaviors. For each quality you plan to observe, define what is meant by an exceptional, acceptable, and poor performance.
- Let the students know how and when you will be observing them.
- Use the evaluation forms as checklists. You can write comments in the appropriate boxes or assign a numeric value to each level of performance. The following scale might be convenient:

  exceptional = 5 or 6 points
  acceptable = 3 or 4 points
  poor = 1 or 2 points

Name _____ Group _____

Standards for Evaluating a Cooperative Activity

Assigned Role   recorder   reporter   materials manager   discussion leader   other _____
(circle one)

Group Cooperation	Exceptional	Acceptable	Poor
1. Helps resolve conflicts to maintain agreement			
2. Shares responsibility for the activity			
3. Uses group time productively			
4. Helps the group stay on task			
5. Helps the group complete the activity			
Individual Performance			
6. Communicates ideas and concerns clearly			
7. Cooperates with other group members			
8. Fulfills assigned role			
9. Contributes ideas and effort to the group			
10. Is comfortable working with peers			
11. Demonstrates ability to motivate others			

Comments _____

_____

_____

Overall rating _____

Standards for Evaluating a Group Discussion

Cooperation	Exceptional	Acceptable	Poor
1. Freely participates in discussion			
2. Listens carefully and respectfully to others			
3. Shares personal opinions			
4. Displays tolerance for different opinions			
5. Contributes appropriate ideas and suggestions			
Individual Performance			
6. Is prepared			
7. Stays on task during discussion			
8. Communicates ideas clearly			
9. Supports own point of view with reasons or evidence			
10. Shows confidence in own judgment			
11. Demonstrates ability to modify thinking			

Comments _____

_____

_____

_____

Overall rating _____

Chapter 3

Product and Performance Assessment: Looking at the Final Results

In product and performance assessment, the student is required to develop a tangible product or performance as evidence of learning. Traditionally products and performances have been assessed and graded by the teacher working after the product is complete. Alternative assessment of products and performances calls for ongoing communication with students about goals and standards and for the assessment of a wider range of products than might previously have been considered.

Characteristics of Product and Performance Assessment

1. Product and performance assessment places the emphasis on the final results rather than on the process by which a student reached the results. As an evaluator, you need to separate the process from the end result in making your assessment.

2. Products or performances can be short-term or long-term, taking a class period, several days or weeks, or even several months to complete.

3. Students can do projects alone or in groups.

4. Products and performances are often multi-part, involving several stages, components, and tasks. For that reason, the final result is apt to be as successful as the planning and organizing that the student puts into it.

Ensuring Success

Some students enjoy projects, while others find the less-structured project format to be stressful. You can help ensure that all students succeed by providing guidance during the planning stages.

1. Provide students with a list of performance and product formats from which they can choose. Try to give students enough different options so they can find products that match their preferred learning modes. (Examples of products and performances are listed below.)

2. Introduce proposals as a way for students to get focused. A sample Project Proposal and Action Plan appears on page 11.

3. Have students prepare task sheets and progress reports. By looking at the whole process before they begin a project, and by evaluating their progress as they go along, students will make better decisions about how to proceed. The Task Sheet on page 12 can be used for these purposes.

4. Allow students to work individually at times and in small groups at other times so that you can get a rounded picture of their capabilities and achievements.

Examples of Products and Performances

advertisement	cooking	flow chart	painting/drawing	scrapbook
architectural design	demonstration	game	pamphlet	script
audiotape	correspondence	graph	panel discussion	scroll
biography	costume	interview	pantomime	sculpture
book review	crafts	invention	petition	short story
brochure	dance	map	photograph album	skit
bulletin board	debate	memoir	play	slide show
chart	diorama	mobile	poem	song
children's book	directory	mock trial	poster	speech
collage	editorial	mosaic	rap	survey
collection	essay	mural	recital	time capsule
comic strip	eulogy	museum	research paper	time line
computer program	family tree	musical instrument	role-play	videotape
constitution	flag	news story	scale model	
contract	flip chart	oral history	scenery for a play	

Assessing Progress

When using products and performances for assessment purposes, be sure you have appropriate evaluation instruments. The following examples may help you.

1. Require periodic progress reports.

2. Establish criteria for a successful product or performance through rubrics and other devices. Suggested criteria for evaluating performances and products appear in Chapter 5, Rubrics for Activity Options, pp. 24-35.

   • In each unit, a History Workshop provides a hands-on project that is appropriate for product assessment.

   • The Teacher's Edition provides standards for evaluating the section activities options, the chapter assessment options, and the Interdisciplinary Challenges.

3. Ask students to develop their own rubrics using the Rubrics for Activity Options as a starting point,

4. Incorporate peer review as part of the assessment process. A sample format for Peer Assessment appears on page 13.

5. Include self-assessment at every stage of the assessment process. Encourage your students to reflect on their learning styles, habits, and strengths. A sample format for Self-Assessment appears on page 14.

Support for Product and Performance Assessment in *Creating America*

Creating America provides opportunities for product and performance assessment throughout the program.

• At the beginning of each chapter, students are asked to complete an Interact with History activity.

• In each chapter assessment students are given three alternative assessment activities to complete individually or in small groups.

• The Teacher's Edition provides standards for evaluating the section activities options, the chapter assessment options, and the Interdisciplinary Challenges.

• *In-Depth Resources* for each unit provides Primary Sources and Literature Selections with suggested activities that often produce a project or performance.

Using the Forms to Assess Products and Performances

• Work with students to create the rubric you will use to evaluate behaviors. For each quality you plan to assess, define what is meant by an exceptional, acceptable, and poor performance.

• Let the students know how and when you will be assessing their work.

• Use the evaluation forms as checklists. You can write comments in the appropriate boxes or assign a numeric value to each level of performance. The following scale might be convenient:

   exceptional = 5 or 6 points
   acceptable = 3 or 4 points
   poor = 1 or 2 points

Product and Performance Assessment

Project Proposal and Action Plan

Directions: Use this form to help think through and organize your work.

My topic _____

I expect to discover or communicate _____

I plan to work alone _____ or with _____

I plan to demonstrate what I've learned by creating a/an

_____ audiotape/videotape   _____ skit, play, or script

_____ drawing, painting, or diagram   _____ book or movie review

_____ series of photographs   _____ other _____

_____ essay or report

I plan to use the following resources

_____ books, magazines   _____ interviews

_____ CD-ROM, Internet   _____ other _____

The basic steps I will take are as follows:

1. _____

2. _____

3. _____

4. _____

5. _____

6. _____

Group _____   Project _____   Date _____

Product and Performance Assessment

Task Sheet for a Group Project

Directions: Use this form to plan and organize your group's project. First list the steps you will take in the left-hand column. Then assign each task to a group member, and list a reasonable target date for completing each task. Finally make a note of materials you will need.

Steps and Tasks	Who Will Do Each Task	Target Date	Materials Needed
Planning			
Research			
Development			
Presentation of Product			

Peer Assessment

Directions: Listen carefully as your classmates make their presentations. Write the titles of the presentations and the names of the presenters in the spaces below. Then use the rating scale in the right-hand column to evaluate their work. Circle the number that best expresses your rating of each part of the performance. (A rating of 3 is exceptional, 2 is acceptable, and 1 is poor.)

Presentation Titles	Presenters	Your Rating		
		Purpose	3 2 1	
		Treatment of Subject	3 2 1	
		Resources Used	3 2 1	
		Product/Exhibition	3 2 1	
		Presentation	3 2 1	
		Purpose	3 2 1	
		Treatment of Subject	3 2 1	
		Resources Used	3 2 1	
		Product/Exhibition	3 2 1	
		Presentation	3 2 1	
		Purpose	3 2 1	
		Treatment of Subject	3 2 1	
		Resources Used	3 2 1	
		Product/Exhibition	3 2 1	
		Presentation	3 2 1	

What are the most interesting things you learned from each presentation?

_____

_____

_____

Product and Performance Assessment

Self-Assessment

Directions: After you have completed a project or made a presentation, use this form to reflect on your work. Fill in the boxes to answer the questions at the left.

1. Imagine that someone from another school asked you about your project. How would you describe what you did?	
2. What steps did you take to get the project done?	
3. Do you feel good about the results? Why or why not?	
4. Did you work with others? If so, how did you divide the work? Did the group work well together?	
5. What was the best thing for you about the project?	
6. Are there any things you would do differently if you did the project again? Please explain.	
7. What advice would you give another student who is planning a project similar to yours?	

Portfolio Assessment: Compiling a Collection

An assessment portfolio is a collection of student work that demonstrates effort, progress, and achievement over time. It is analogous to the portfolios used by artists, writers, photographers, and architects in the professional world. Portfolios enable students to review the progress they have made and to evaluate the products they have created. In selecting samples of their work to be assembled into a portfolio, students answer such questions as: Which work shows the best I can do? Which work shows the progress I have made? Which work demonstrates the variety of things I can do?

Using portfolios for assessment is a practice that has become increasingly popular in schools as a way to focus on student growth and development. In contrast to traditional forms of assessment, portfolios are ongoing and they require student involvement.

Portfolios provide teachers and students with feedback about the process of learning and therefore play a role in instruction as well as in assessment. Teachers and students can review the portfolio contents together to see how well the student is learning and what he or she needs to review.

Characteristics of Portfolios

Effective portfolios share the following characteristics.

- A portfolio has a clear purpose, established early in the year and understood by the teacher and the students.
- Portfolios are selective; they are not holders for all of a student's work.
- Students must be involved in selecting the portfolio contents.
- Criteria for selecting and judging portfolio contents must be established early.
- Portfolios must contain evidence of self-assessment and reflection, showing what students know about themselves and their work. This evidence can take the form of letters, notes to the teacher, or other devices that students develop.

- Portfolios are usually chronological, demonstrating a student's growth and development over time.
- Portfolios often include a wide array of student work, capturing the depth and breadth of a student's understanding.

Setting Up Portfolio Assessment

The following are steps to take in establishing portfolio assessment in your classroom. Remember that portfolios evolve throughout the year; you may want to revisit the decisions you make at the beginning once you discover how the process is working for you and your students.

Establish a Purpose for Using Portfolios

Decide what purpose you wish the portfolios to serve. Common purposes include the following:

- to examine the teaching and learning of history reading as a process
- to examine the teaching and learning of writing about history
- to examine the growth of understanding over time
- to examine the development of critical thinking skills over time
- to assess the ability of students to apply what they have learned
- to focus students' attention on a particular area of concentration
- to help students prepare for a major research project or examination

Decide on a Type of Portfolio to Use

Teachers typically use one or more of four common types of portfolios.

A *working portfolio* is a record of a student's work in a particular class. It contains a collection of student products, performances, and test results over a given period of time. The intent is usually to accumulate final results rather than to reflect on the development processes. Often a working portfolio becomes a resource for a showcase portfolio.

A *showcase portfolio* includes selected examples of a student's best work. It features products and performances that go beyond paper-and-pencil worksheets and tests. Often the work meets clearly stated learning objectives and criteria. Self-reflection is especially important for this type of portfolio. Typically the student and the teacher both write reflective pieces explaining why they consider the work to be the student's best.

The *process portfolio* shows a student's work in all its stages, up to and including the final results. In a process portfolio, students keep all the evidence of a work in progress. The collection can include planning documents, drafts, notes from peer and teacher conferences, reflections on stages of the process, and the final product or performance. An excellent vehicle for communication between teacher and student, a process portfolio can become the basis for meaningful process assessment. This portfolio can also become a resource for a showcase portfolio.

The *cumulative* or *archival portfolio* shows a student's best work over several years. Examples are typically drawn from a showcase portfolio and include a student's reflections on the work. Periodic maintenance is necessary so the collection doesn't become unwieldy. A cumulative portfolio can demonstrate a student's growth and development over an extended period of time.

Decide on a Selection Process

Will the portfolio be all student-selected? Part student-selected and part prescribed? Negotiated by teacher and student? What will be the role of parents and the administration? Regardless of what you decide, always allow students full participation in the selection process.

Use Portfolio Contents on page 18 and Portfolio Reflection on page 19 to help students select and organize their work into meaningful collections.

Create an Evaluation and Assessment Process

Will there be minimum standards for inclusion of materials? What will be the process for evaluation? Be sure to consider evaluation standards and discuss them with students at the beginning so everyone will understand expectations.

Share your criteria for portfolio evaluation with students at the beginning of the process. If possible, develop those criteria together. Use Portfolio Reflection on page 19 and Self-Assessment on page 22 to help guide students through the evaluation process. Use Sample Rubric for a Portfolio and Standards for Evaluating a Portfolio on pages 20 and 21 to conduct your own evaluation. Finally, send home Family Response on page 23 to involve family members in the portfolio process.

Decide on a Time Frame

At the beginning of the school year, lay out a schedule that includes dates for getting started, adding student work to portfolios, reviewing criteria for evaluation with the students, selecting final contents of portfolios, and conferencing with students.

Make Practical Decisions for Portfolio Maintenance

How will the materials actually be stored? Portfolios can look as varied as the students who put them together. They can be kept in hanging files, folders, boxes, baskets, crates, drawers, or on tapes or computer disks.

Who will maintain the portfolios? Avoid being the warehouse manager for student portfolios. Student ownership is an important part of portfolio assessment, and students should assume responsibility for their materials.

What will happen to the portfolios at the end of the year? This is likely to be a school- or districtwide decision. Decide or find out before you start. If any materials are retained from year to year, make sure they are the ones most representative of the student's work.

Possible Work to Include in a Portfolio

Work in progress	Finished work	Reading items	Other
journal entries	revised pieces	summaries	artwork
class notes	research reports	reading record	maps
prewriting exercises	essay question	Guided Reading	models
rough drafts	answers	worksheets	diagrams
revisions	dramatic readings	outlines	photographs
tape recordings	poems	book reviews	tape recordings
or videotapes of	oral report outlines		videotapes
group work	scripts of simulations		letters

Support for Product and Portfolio Assessment in *Creating America*

Creating America provides ample opportunities for portfolio assessment throughout the program.

- At the end of each chapter in *Creating America*, students are given two portfolio options.
- The Teacher's Edition provides standards for evaluating each of the portfolio options.
- *In-Depth Resources* for each unit provide Primary Sources and Literature Selections with suggested activities that could be used in portfolios.
- Section Assessments and Chapter Assessment Alternative Activities provide opportunities for portfolio items.
- *Interdisciplinary Challenges* have activities that might be included in a portfolio.

Using the Forms to Assess Portfolios

- Work with students to create the rubric you will use to evaluate behaviors. For each quality you plan to evaluate, define what is meant by an exceptional, acceptable, and poor performance.
- Let the students know how and when you will be assessing their work.
- Use the evaluation forms as checklists. You can write comments in the appropriate boxes or assign a numeric value to each level of performance. The following scale might be convenient:

  exceptional = 5 or 6 points;
  acceptable = 3 or 4 points;
  poor = 1 or 2 points

Name _____   Date _____

Portfolio Contents

Directions: Use this form to keep track of your portfolio contents and your reasons for including each piece. Once you have completed the selection process, make a separate table of contents from this list.

Date	Work Added to Portfolio	Why I feel good about it or what I learned from it

Portfolio Reflection

Directions: Use this form to summarize your feelings about the pieces you have chosen for your portfolio.

1. Which piece was the easiest for me to do?   _____

2. Which piece was the hardest for me to do?   _____

3. Which piece shows the most improvement?   _____

4. Which piece makes me most proud?   _____

5. Which piece shows the most creativity?   _____

6. Which piece was the most fun to do?   _____

7. Which piece do I like the most?   _____

8. Which piece do I expect my teacher to like the most?   _____

9. Which piece do I think my family will like the most?

10. Which piece would I like to do over again in order to improve it?   _____

11. What do I want my teacher to notice most about my portfolio?   _____

12. What do I want my family to notice most about my portfolio?   _____

13. If I had more time, what would I change about my portfolio?

_____

_____

_____

_____

Sample Rubric for a Portfolio

Directions: Teachers: Before assessing a portfolio read and consider the following descriptions of standards for evaluation. Students: Before compiling a portfolio, become familiar with the qualities on which your performance will be evaluated.

Quality	Exceptional	Acceptable	Poor
Versatility	Collection shows a wide range of interests and abilities.	Collection shows an average range of interests and abilities.	Collection shows little range of interests and abilities.
Reflections	Reflections are thoughtful. The student reveals strong insights about areas of strength and the need for improvement and indicates clear goals for the future.	Reflections are reasonable. The student shows some insights about areas of strength and the need for improvement and indicates reasonable goals for the future.	Reflections show little attention. Insights are lacking about areas of strength and the need for improvement. The student lacks goals for the future.
Improvement	Samples show thoughtful attention to process. They indicate that the student has grown from the experience of creating and reviewing the work.	Samples show some attention to process. They indicate that the student has gained somewhat from the experience of creating and reviewing the work.	Samples lack an understanding of process. They indicate the student has learned little from the experience of creating and reviewing the work.
Problem Solving	Samples indicate that the student recognizes his or her own problems or responds to those that are pointed out. The student shows resourcefulness in solving problems.	Samples indicate that the student recognizes some problems or responds to some problems when they are pointed out. The student shows some resourcefulness in solving problems.	Samples show the student's unwillingness or inability to deal with problems. The student does not identify his or her own problems or ignores those pointed out.
Content, Form, and Mechanics	The student shows careful attention to the final product. Content, form, and mechanics show strong control.	The student shows adequate attention to the final product. Content, form, and mechanics show growing command.	The student shows little or no attention to the final product. Content, form, and mechanics show a need for significant improvement.

Name _____ Date _____

Standards for Evaluating a Portfolio

Versatility	Exceptional	Acceptable	Poor
1. Demonstrates a wide range of abilities.			
2. Demonstrates a wide range of interests.			
3. Approaches each task creatively.			
Reflections			
4. Has made careful selections for the portfolio.			
5. Has explained his or her selections clearly.			
6. Has reached valuable insights about the work.			
Improvement			
7. Has made significant improvement.			
8. Recognizes where the work could be further improved.			
9. Shows an interest and willingness to improve.			
Problem Solving			
10. Recognizes problems with his or her work.			
11. Shows resourcefulness in solving problems.			
Content, Form, and Mechanics			
12. Shows careful attention to quality.			
13. Shows strong control over content, form, and mechanics.			

Comments _____

_____

_____

Overall rating_____

Portfolio Assessment

Self-Assessment

Directions: Discuss with your teacher the criteria for evaluating portfolios, then use this form to evaluate your own.

1. What are the standards that will be used by your teacher to evaluate the work in your portfolio?

    _____

2. Do you think these standards are complete and fair? If not, what would you change about them?

    _____

3. Thinking about the work you have collected, what makes you proud of your portfolio?

    _____

4. In general, what would you change about the work in your portfolio?

    _____

5. Which piece makes you the happiest? Why?

    _____

6. Which piece gave you the most trouble? Describe the trouble you had with it.

    _____

7. Which piece would you like to do over again, and how would you improve it?

    _____

8. Which piece was the most enjoyable to do?

    _____

9. Which piece do you think is your most creative?

    _____

10. In the future, what kinds of work would you like to do more often?

    _____

11. Comparing your earlier work with your later work, do you see improvement? Describe the differences you see.

    _____

12. What have you learned by selecting and evaluating the pieces in your portfolio? Describe the experience.

    _____

Name _____   Date _____

Family Response

Directions: Discuss with your student the purpose of his or her portfolio, then use this form to give your own impressions of your student's work.

1. My first impression of the portfolio was

   _____

   _____

2. As I read the pieces in the portfolio, I learned

   _____

   _____

3. I was especially pleased to see

   _____

   _____

4. I was surprised to find out

   _____

   _____

5. I noticed growth and improvement in these areas:

   _____

   _____

   _____

6. I noticed a need for further work or help in these areas:

   _____

   _____

7. I had the following questions after looking through the portfolio:

   _____

   _____

8. My overall impression after studying the portfolio is

   _____

   _____

Rubrics for Activity Options

To the Teacher

Creating America provides you with Activity Options at the end of every section. These activities offer a full range of alternative assessment opportunities across the subject areas. In the pages that follow you will find rubrics to help you assess those Activity Options. The activities fall into five main categories. Below you will find a rationale for each of the five main categories. On the pages listed you will find the general and specific evaluation standards you may use to assess your students for each activity category.

1. Art Type Activities pp. 25-27

These activities allow students to express thoughts and ideas by using two- and three-dimensional materials. You may evaluate how well the product demonstrates an understanding of the ideas presented. You may also evaluate the artistic worth of the product.

2. Information Assessing Activities pp. 28-29

These activities are designed to give students an opportunity to show how well they can collect and assess data, and then present that information in a presentation form. You can evaluate on both the correctness of information assessment and the presentation of that information to others.

3. Oral Presentations pp. 30-31

These activities involve speaking or acting in front of a group. Some of the activities are prepared in advance, while others require thinking and speaking as a debate or discussion unfolds. You may want to evaluate not only what the student knows but how well she or he is able to communicate with others.

4. Writing Activities pp. 32-33

These activities give the student an opportunity to express ideas in written language. Some of the activities require imagination, and others require students to develop opinions on a topic. You may evaluate how clearly and completely the student is able to present ideas.

5. Technology Activities pp. 34-35

Technology activities involve using technical equipment to do research and to make presentations about what students have learned. For some of the activities, students will create material to be recorded or to be presented on screen. You may evaluate the student's ability to clearly present information and to use technology in a skillful manner.

Art Type Activities

General Criteria/Guidelines for Evaluation

The art should

- help to present the information in a style that will aid the viewer in understanding the information.
- use pictures, words, and symbols to explain each step in a process and the relationship between them.
- be presented clearly, possibly with the use of conventional images.
- be neatly presented and creative.
- should be in order chronologically and must remain historically correct and accurate.
- express the artist's views in a clear/concise manner.

Specific Criteria/Guidelines for Evaluation

These guidelines will help you evaluate specific art type activities.

1.1 *Poster*

	Excellent				Poor
• Conveys a concept through effective visuals	5	4	3	2	1
• Uses persuasive language in slogans or memorable sentences	5	4	3	2	1
• Targets a specific audience	5	4	3	2	1
• Is presented neatly	5	4	3	2	1

1.2 *Political Cartoon*

	Excellent				Poor
• Presents a concept clearly, possibly with the use of conventional images	5	4	3	2	1
• Has a title	5	4	3	2	1
• Is presented neatly	5	4	3	2	1

1.3 *Illustration/diagram picture/scene/comic strip/cartoons*

	Excellent				Poor
• Represents the specific idea or concept in a manner clear to the viewers	5	4	3	2	1
• Exhibits creativity	5	4	3	2	1
• Demonstrates grade level artistic skill	5	4	3	2	1
• Is presented neatly	5	4	3	2	1

1.4 *Art Depicting a Monument*

	Excellent				Poor
• Represents the specific idea or concept in a manner clear to the viewers	5	4	3	2	1
• Exhibits creativity	5	4	3	2	1
• Is presented neatly	5	4	3	2	1

1.5 *Museum exhibit*

	Excellent				Poor
• Has a complete introductory overview	5	4	3	2	1
• Contains accurate and well-described textual information	5	4	3	2	1
• Uses a variety of media	5	4	3	2	1
• May be accompanied by well-informed and lively student presenters	5	4	3	2	1
• Is presented neatly	5	4	3	2	1

1.6 *Storyboard*

	Excellent				Poor
• Presents a story in segments	5	4	3	2	1
• Includes specific sound, light, or other cues	5	4	3	2	1
• Exhibits creativity	5	4	3	2	1
• Is presented neatly	5	4	3	2	1

1.7 *Trading Card*

	Excellent				Poor
• Has a picture, drawing or caricature of the person on one side	5	4	3	2	1
• Has additional information about the person on one side	5	4	3	2	1
• Is presented neatly	5	4	3	2	1

1.8 *Collage*

	Excellent				Poor
• Demonstrates an understanding of the concept	5	4	3	2	1
• Presents a concept clearly through juxtapositions of words or pictures	5	4	3	2	1
• Is presented neatly	5	4	3	2	1

1.9 *Mobiles*

	Excellent				Poor
• Demonstrates an understanding of the concept	5	4	3	2	1
• Presents the concept clearly through the positioning of pictures, and or words	5	4	3	2	1
• Is put together neatly and balances when hung	5	4	3	2	1

1.10 *Replica or Model*

	Excellent				Poor
• Represents the specific idea or concept in 2 or 3 dimensional manner clear to the viewers	5	4	3	2	1
• Exhibits creativity	5	4	3	2	1
• Demonstrates grade level artistic skill	5	4	3	2	1
• Is presented neatly	5	4	3	2	1

1.11 *Mural*

	Excellent				Poor
• Drawing/illustration should accurately portray historical events	5	4	3	2	1
• The oral presentation should present additional information about the events pictured	5	4	3	2	1
• The project shows effort by each member of the group	5	4	3	2	1
• Is presented neatly	5	4	3	2	1

1.12 *Board game*

	Excellent				Poor
• The selected events reflect an understanding of the time period	5	4	3	2	1
• The events are chronologically correct	5	4	3	2	1
• The rules are clear to the players	5	4	3	2	1
• The game board is attractive and neatly done	5	4	3	2	1

1.13 *Brochure/leaflet*

	Excellent				Poor
• Represents the specific idea or concept in a manner clear to the viewers	5	4	3	2	1
• Clearly states a position about the issue	5	4	3	2	1
• Presents supporting reasons for their position	5	4	3	2	1
• Exhibits creativity	5	4	3	2	1
• Demonstrates grade level artistic skill	5	4	3	2	1
• Is presented neatly	5	4	3	2	1

Information Assessing Activities

General Criteria/Guidelines for Evaluation

Information-assessing activities should

- clearly state the purpose of the investigation along with who participated and the procedures used.
- include accurate and factually based information. All information, graphics, statistics, or maps may require documentation.
- fully evaluate the information, and an in-depth analysis should then be given.
- use a compare and contrast method for evaluations.
- include a conclusion drawn based upon the factual evidence and a personal reaction/recommendation from the researcher.
- use correct grammar, usage, capitalization, punctuation, and spelling in written text.

Specific Criteria/Guidelines for Evaluation

These guidelines will help you evaluate specific information assessing activities.

2.1 *Map*

	Excellent				Poor
• Clearly labeled and neatly presented	5	4	3	2	1
• Includes a legend and title	5	4	3	2	1
• Include either or both physical and political locations	5	4	3	2	1
• If a series—should clearly show changes that occurred	5	4	3	2	1

2.2 *Chart/ Table*

	Excellent				Poor
• Presents information accurately	5	4	3	2	1
• Presents information in a style that will aid the viewer in understanding the information	5	4	3	2	1
• Is presented neatly	5	4	3	2	1

2.3 *Graph*

	Excellent				Poor
• Presents information accurately	5	4	3	2	1
• Uses bar, line, or pie styles	5	4	3	2	1
• Presents information in a style that will aid the viewer in understanding the information	5	4	3	2	1
• Is presented neatly	5	4	3	2	1

2.4 *Time Line*

	Excellent				Poor
• Is organized chronologically	5	4	3	2	1
• Events and illustrations are clearly described	5	4	3	2	1
• Is presented neatly	5	4	3	2	1

2.5 *Report*

	Excellent				Poor
• Has a thesis	5	4	3	2	1
• Clearly states facts and examples to support major points	5	4	3	2	1
• Has a bibliography	5	4	3	2	1
• Uses correct grammar, spelling, and punctuation	5	4	3	2	1

2.6 *Database*

	Excellent				Poor
• Presents a variety of information from several sources	5	4	3	2	1
• Presents information accurately	5	4	3	2	1
• Clearly identifies sources of information	5	4	3	2	1

2.7 *Poll/Survey*

	Excellent				Poor
• Has a clear purpose and goals	5	4	3	2	1
• Is unbiased in its coverage	5	4	3	2	1
• Has a clearly presented summary of results	5	4	3	2	1
• Uses correct grammar, spelling, and punctuation	5	4	3	2	1

Oral Presentations

General Criteria/Guidelines for Evaluation

An oral presentation should
- have a clearly stated the problem, position, or topic.
- have a clear focus throughout, and all organization should be logical.
- capture the audience's attention with an interesting introduction.
- give appropriate background and research information, and use it to defend the position.
- highlight especially interesting or unusual details.
- include some personal reactions and feelings if appropriate.
- contain a conclusion that summarizes the main points and restates the speaker's position and contains commentary or conclusions about the subject.

Specific Criteria/Guidelines for Evaluation

These guidelines will help you evaluate specific oral presentation activities.

3.1 *Dramatic Scene/Skit/Play*

	Excellent				Poor
Accurately portrays the event(s) selected	5	4	3	2	1
Conveys information through visuals and through performance	5	4	3	2	1
Exhibits creativity in creating the scene	5	4	3	2	1
Shows evidence of involvement of each person in the group	5	4	3	2	1

3.2 *Panel Discussion*

	Excellent				Poor
Discussion has a central question or topic	5	4	3	2	1
Students support their own positions with evidence or logic	5	4	3	2	1
Students appropriately respond to each other's statements	5	4	3	2	1

3.3 *Interview /Press Conference*

	Excellent				Poor
Questions reflect a selected focus	5	4	3	2	1
Questions reflect the student's understanding of basic concepts relevant to the experiences of the person selected	5	4	3	2	1
Answers accurately reflect the thoughts and experiences of the subject's life	5	4	3	2	1

3.4 *Debate*   Excellent   Poor

- Debate has a central question or proposition   5   4   3   2   1
- Students support their own positions and refute their opponent's position with evidence   5   4   3   2   1
- Students appropriately respond to each other's statements   5   4   3   2   1

3.5 *Living Biography*   Excellent   Poor

- Objects clearly represent the individual being portrayed   5   4   3   2   1
- Presentation gives adequate clues to the identity of the person   5   4   3   2   1
- Presentation reflects an historical understanding of the significance of the individual   5   4   3   2   1

3.6 *Speech/Oral Report/Oral History*   Excellent   Poor

- Information presented reflects the student's understanding of basic concepts or ideas relevant to the topic   5   4   3   2   1
- Presentation has a clear introduction and conclusion   5   4   3   2   1
- Presentation has adequate delivery and establishes rapport with the audience   5   4   3   2   1

Writing Activities

General Criteria/Guidelines for Evaluation

A written presentation should
- be clear, focused, and logical.
- have an attention grabbing introduction that clearly states the topic and purpose, along with a strong conclusion to end the piece.
- clearly state student's purpose, idea, or opinion and provide necessary facts and examples to support them.
- present both sides of an issue and then strategically reject and refute the counter argument with facts and a persuasive style.
- show a deep understanding of the character, times, or other aspects of the topic.
- use interesting and creative style. The writing should either engage or aim to educate the reader depending on the topic.
- follow the rules of spelling, punctuation, grammar along with proper paragraph usage.

Specific Criteria/Guidelines for Evaluation

These guidelines will help you evaluate specific writing activities.

4.1 *Editorial/Letter to the Editor/Opinion Article*

	Excellent				Poor
• Clearly states a position about the issue	5	4	3	2	1
• Presents supporting reasons for the position	5	4	3	2	1
• Clearly rebuts other viewpoints	5	4	3	2	1
• Uses correct grammar, spelling, and punctuation	5	4	3	2	1

4.2 *Essay*

	Excellent				Poor
• Begins with an introduction and has a thesis	5	4	3	2	1
• Presents supporting reasons for the evaluation	5	4	3	2	1
• Clearly draws a conclusion that supports the thesis	5	4	3	2	1
• Uses correct grammar, spelling, and punctuation	5	4	3	2	1

4.3 *Diary /Journal Entry/Letter*

	Excellent				Poor
• Accurately reflects the thoughts and experiences of the subject's life	5	4	3	2	1
• Covers important periods of the subject's life	5	4	3	2	1
• Reflects the student's understanding of basic concepts	5	4	3	2	1
• Uses correct grammar, spelling, and punctuation	5	4	3	2	1

4.4 *Biography*

	Excellent				Poor
• Accurately conveys information about the subject's life	5	4	3	2	1
• Is logically organized	5	4	3	2	1
• Is written in an interesting style	5	4	3	2	1
• Uses correct grammar, spelling, and punctuation	5	4	3	2	1

4.5 *News Article/Mock Magazine/Description*

	Excellent				Poor
• Uses a journalistic style	5	4	3	2	1
• Presents information in an unbiased way	5	4	3	2	1
• Covers the topic adequately	5	4	3	2	1
• Each article has a headline and presents and portrays the historical events accurately	5	4	3	2	1
• Layout is neatly presented	5	4	3	2	1
• Uses correct grammar, spelling, and punctuation	5	4	3	2	1

4.6 *Story*

	Excellent				Poor
• Reflect the student's understanding of basic concepts	5	4	3	2	1
• Relevant to the experiences of the subject	5	4	3	2	1
• Uses correct grammar, spelling, and punctuation	5	4	3	2	1

4.7 *Book Report/Review*

	Excellent				Poor
• Includes an introduction that identifies the book and states a response to the work	5	4	3	2	1
• Supports the response with evidence from the book	5	4	3	2	1
• Uses language and details that are appropriate for the audience	5	4	3	2	1
• Uses correct grammar, spelling, and punctuation	5	4	3	2	1

4.8 *Poem/Musical Lyrics/Song*

	Excellent				Poor
• Shows an understanding of the topic or issue	5	4	3	2	1
• Uses appropriate elements of poetry, such as images and symbolism	5	4	3	2	1
• Uses appropriate lyrics possibly containing rhythm and rhyme and connecting to musical phrasing	5	4	3	2	1

4.9 *Advertisement*

	Excellent				Poor
• Clearly presents persuasive reasons for supporting the goal	5	4	3	2	1
• Uses persuasive language in slogans or memorable sentences	5	4	3	2	1
• Utilizes colorful language and verbal images	5	4	3	2	1
• Uses correct grammar in the script or print ads	5	4	3	2	1

Technology Activities

General Criteria/Guidelines for Evaluation

Presentations using technology should

- either engage or aim to educate the viewer depending on the topic.
- use an interesting and creative style.
- use interesting images and/or audio elements to make points in multi-media presentation.
- show a deep understanding of the character, times, topic, etc.
- contain links and written summaries on a web page that will encourage browsers to visit other web sites.
- exhibit the ability to correctly use the technology.

Specific Criteria/Guidelines for Evaluation

These guidelines will help you evaluate specific writing activities.

5.1 *Web Page*   Excellent   Poor

	Excellent				Poor
• Contains at least 3 links	5	4	3	2	1
• Makes effective use of pictures and icons	5	4	3	2	1
• Contains written summaries that will encourage browsers to visit other web sites	5	4	3	2	1
• Shows technical proficiency	5	4	3	2	1

5.2 *Media Campaign*   Excellent   Poor

	Excellent				Poor
• Clearly presents persuasive reasons for supporting the goal	5	4	3	2	1
• Utilizes a variety of media	5	4	3	2	1
• Uses correct grammar in the script or print materials	5	4	3	2	1

5.3 *Video/Audio Presentation*   Excellent   Poor

	Excellent				Poor
• Portrays the historical event accurately and in a dramatic style	5	4	3	2	1
• Clearly demonstrates an understanding of the concepts presented	5	4	3	2	1
• Shows technical proficiency	5	4	3	2	1

5.4 *Multi-media Presentation/ Electronic Presentation*

	Excellent				Poor
• Utilizes two or more media	5	4	3	2	1
• Clearly demonstrates an understanding of the concepts presented	5	4	3	2	1
• Shows technical proficiency	5	4	3	2	1

5.5 *Documentary*

	Excellent				Poor
• Is organized chronologically	5	4	3	2	1
• Portrays the historical event accurately and in a dramatic style	5	4	3	2	1
• Uses standard interview techniques	5	4	3	2	1
• Uses correct grammar in script	5	4	3	2	1

5.6 *Spreadsheet*

	Excellent				Poor
• Presents information accurately	5	4	3	2	1
• Uses a format that aids the viewer in accessing the information	5	4	3	2	1
• Shows technical proficiency	5	4	3	2	1